WORKBOOK

CONTEMPORARY ENGLISH
BOOK 2

Jeanne Becijos

Mechelle Perrott

Cecelia Ryan

CONTEMPORARY BOOKS

a division of NTC/CONTEMPORARY PUBLISHING GROUP
Lincolnwood, Illinois USA

Cover Illustration: Regan Dunnick

Interior Illustrations: April Mosakowski

ISBN: 0-8092-0721-4

Published by Contemporary Books,
a division of NTC/Contemporary Publishing Group, Inc.
© 1999 NTC/Contemporary Publishing Group, Inc.,
4255 West Touhy Avenue, Lincolnwood (Chicago), Illinois 60646-1975 U.S.A.

Manufactured in the United States of America.

890 V P 0 9 8 7 6 5 4 3 2 1

Contents

About the Workbooks

Contemporary English is a five-level interactive topic-based English-as-a-Second-Language series for adult learners ranging from the beginning-literacy level to the high-intermediate level. The *Contemporary English* Workbooks are designed for individual independent study as well as for classroom work. In the Workbooks, as in the Student Books, a predictable sequence is maintained.

For ease of use, the essential information in the **Spotlight** boxes of the Student Books is reproduced in the Workbooks. Each **Spotlight** is followed by a series of contextualized practice exercises, progressing from simple fill-ins to more challenging activities that ask students to use the target structures as they write answers to real-life questions about themselves. Answers to all Workbook activities can be found in the Teacher's Manual.

The **Read, Think, and Write** pages at the end of each Workbook unit synthesize skills presented and practiced in the unit in an engaging multi-stage activity. The reading is supported by pre- and post-reading questions. After the reading, one or two activities ask learners to organize the information, usually with the same type of graphic organizer used in **Wrap-Up** in the Student Book. The final problem-solving activity challenges learners to apply the content to their own lives. Each unit closes with a brief questionnaire, similar to **Think About Learning** in the Student Book, in which students note what was most enjoyable and helpful in the Workbook.

In short, the *Contemporary English* Workbooks provide the additional practice students need, in an easy-to-use, interesting format.

Spotlight on *Be* in Affirmative and Negative Statements and in Questions

Affirmative		Negative	
I **am**	a student.	I **am not**	a student.
I**'m**	a student	I**'m not**	
He/She/It **is**	11 years old.	He/She/It **is not**	11 years old.
He**'s**/She**'s**/It**'s**		He**'s**/She**'s**/It**'s not**	
You/We/They **are**	in adult school.	You/We/They **are not**	in adult school.
You**'re**/We**'re**/They**'re**		You**'re**/We**'re**/They**'re not**	

Practice I

Mario is talking with the secretary at City Center Adult School. Complete the conversation. Use the words below.

not   isn't   am   is   are   aren't   he's

SECRETARY: _____Are_____ you a new student?

MARIO: No, I'm _____. I _____ here to get an application

for my brother.

SECRETARY: OK. _____ your brother here with you?

MARIO: No, _____ _____. _____ at home.

SECRETARY: This _____ a school for adults.

_____ your brother 18 years old or older?

MARIO: Yes, he _____. He _____ 19 years old.

Practice 2

Answer these questions in your notebook.

1. Is Mario a new student?

2. Are you a student?

3. Is Mario's brother 19 years old?

4. Are you 19 years old?

Practice 3

Read the story. Write a yes/no question for each answer.

Lin Ven is a student at City Center Adult School. Her daughter is in the 6th grade at Lewis Middle School. Lin also has two sons, but they aren't in school yet. Lin takes care of her sons in the daytime. Her husband takes care of the children at night so Lin can go to school. Her children are happy to have their mother in school.

1. _____ Is Lin a teacher? _____

   No, Lin isn't a teacher. She's a student.

2. _____

   No, she isn't in high school. She's in adult school.

3. _____

   Yes, Lin is married.

4. _____

   Yes, her daughter is in the 6th grade.

5. _____

   No, her daughter isn't in elementary school. She's in middle school.

6. _____

   No, her sons aren't in kindergarten. They're not in school yet.

Spotlight on Past of *Be*

Statements	Negatives	Contractions
I **was** happy.	I **was not** sad.	I **wasn't** sad.
You **were** tired.	You **were not** sad.	You **weren't** sad.
She/He **was** angry.	She/He **was not** sad.	She/He **wasn't** sad.
It **was** good.	It **was not** good.	It **wasn't** good.
We **were** happy.	We **were not** sad.	We **weren't** sad.
They **were** happy.	They **were not** sad.	They **weren't** sad.

Questions	Short Answers
Were we/you/they happy?	Yes, I **was.** Yes, we/they **were.**
Was she/he happy?	Yes, she/he **was.**
Was it good?	Yes, it **was.**

Practice 4

Answer the questions about how the person felt.

1. Leonor worked 10 hours yesterday. Was she tired?

   _____ Yes, she was. _____

2. Francisco and his roommate were fighting last week. Were they happy?

   _____

3. Vu was a new student last year. He didn't understand his teacher. Was he confused?

   _____

4. Lin's daughter came home late from school. Was Lin angry?

   _____

5. You found $10 in your coat. Were you surprised?

   _____

Spotlight on the Possessive

Julie and Kathy are Ellen's daughters. = Ellen has two daughters, Julie and Kathy.

Singular Possessive

Mrs. White's 6th grade class (Mrs. White has a 6th grade class.)
Sara's father (Sara has a father.)

Plural Possessive

The students' parents (The students have parents.)
The teachers' students (The teachers have students.)

Practice 5

Complete the sentences below. Use the information in the schedule.

	Samir	Cristina	Chen-Li
9:00	ESL	Math	Chemistry
10:00	History	ESL	History
11:00	Math	Lunch	ESL
12:00	Lunch	Chemistry	Lunch

1. _____Chen-Li's_____ chemistry class starts at 9:00.

2. _____ ESL class starts at 9:00.

3. _____ ESL class is from 10:00 to 11:00.

4. _____ math class starts at 11:00.

5. _____ lunch hour is from 11:00 to 12:00.

6. _____ ESL class starts at 11:00.

7. _____ chemistry class is after lunch.

8. _____ math class is from 11:00 to 12:00.

Read, Think, and Write

Read the story.

School in Two Countries

Juan is from a town in the mountains of Guatemala. He goes to adult school in the United States. He finished his English classes last year. Now he studies in the high school completion program. This program is for students who want to finish high school.

In the United States, most parents want their children to finish high school. In Juan's town in Guatemala, many parents want their children to finish elementary school. Parents need their children at home. They need help with the family farm. Some children go to school at night. They work during the day. They go to school only three times a week. Here in the United States, Juan goes to school five times a week.

In the mountain town in Guatemala, more boys go to school than girls. Most boys learn to read and write. Boys go to the big cities to buy and sell things, but most girls stay home. Many parents don't want girls in school. Juan wants his sisters to study. He sends money to his family. The money helps buy books and pencils for his sisters. His sisters are good students.

Practice 6

Circle the correct answer.

1. Does Juan go to school?

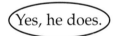 Yes, he does.   No, he doesn't.

2. What does he want to finish?

   elementary school   high school

3. Did Juan finish high school in his country?

   Yes, he did.   No, he didn't.

4. Are there many boys in school in his town?

   Yes, there are.   No, there aren't.

5. Are there many girls in school in his town?

   Yes, there are.   No, there aren't.

Practice 7

How are schools the same around the world? How are they different? Organize your thoughts. Write your ideas in the circles of the idea map. Write two ideas about schools in the United States. Write two ideas about schools in Juan's town. Write two ideas about schools in your native country.

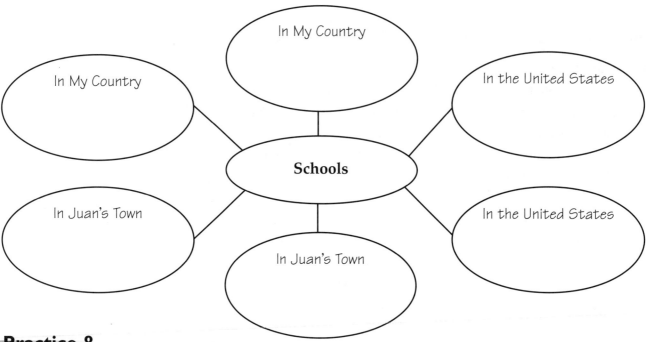

Practice 8

Now look at your idea map. Look for interesting ideas. Write three sentences in your notebook. Write one sentence about school in your country, one sentence about school in the United States, and one sentence about Juan's town in Guatemala.

CHECK YOUR LEARNING

What did you like best about this workbook unit? Why? _____

_____

What did you learn in this workbook unit to help you at work or in

your personal life? _____

_____

Spotlight on Simple Present

Statements		Negative Statements	
I /You/We/They	**play** soccer.	I/You/We/They	**do not (don't) work** on Sunday.
	visit the zoo.		**eat** in restaurants.
	listen to music.		**play** baseball.
	go shopping.		**see** plays.

Janet **goes** to the park.   She **does not (doesn't) like** shopping.
Chan **plays** soccer.   He **does not (doesn't) watch** TV.

Add **-s** to the verb with *he, she* and *it. doesn't = does not   don't = do not*

Practice 1

Complete the stories with the simple present of the verbs.
Use contractions for negative statements.

1. Grace and Antonio (1) *work* _____ hard all week.

   But they (2) *not/work* _____ on the weekends.

   Friday and Saturday they (3) *do* _____ lots of

   activities. Grace (4) *play* _____ tennis with her friend.

   Antonio (5) *listen* _____ to CDs at home.

   At night, they (6) *see* _____ a movie.

   They (7) *not/come* _____ home until 12:00.

   On Sunday their friends often (8) *visit* _____.

2. Gloria and David are friends. But they have problems. Gloria

   (1) *like* _____ museums. David (2) *not/like*

   _____ museums. David (3) *love* _____

   concerts. Gloria (4) *not/like* _____ loud music.

   But they both (5) *like* _____ the park. They

   (6) *visit* _____ the park often.

Spotlight on Verb + Infinitive

	Verb	Infinitive	
Paul	**wants**	**to play**	the guitar.
We	**plan**	**to go**	dancing.
They	**like**	**to go**	to the park.

Practice 2

Use the verbs with infinitives to complete the conversations.

like to listen   plan to go   want to do   want to have   plan to eat

1. **GLORIA:** I (1)_____ *want to do* _____ something this weekend.

   MARTA: I (2)_____ to a concert. Do you

   want to come?

   GLORIA: Sure! I (3)_____ to music.

   When is the concert?

   MARTA: It's at 8:00 Saturday. But I (4)_____

   at a restaurant first. Let's meet at 6:30 P.M. I

   (5)_____ lots of time to eat.

wants to put   plans to swim   plans to camp   wants to hike

2. **PAUL:** What are Chan's plans for next week?

   JANET: He (1)_____ in the mountains.

   PAUL: Oh, really? Where does he usually camp?

   JANET: He (2)_____ his tent near the lake.

   PAUL: Wow, no TV. What does he do all day?

   JANET: He (3)_____ on the mountain and he

   (4)_____ in the lake.

Spotlight on Adverbs of Frequency

I **always** watch TV on the weekends.

We **usually** play soccer.

You **often** go to museums.

She **sometimes** listens to music.

Paul **hardly ever** sees a movie.

Grace **never** plays the piano.

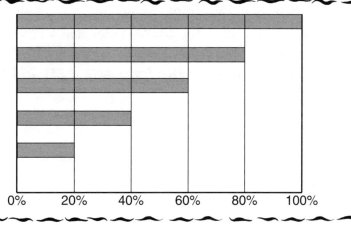

Practice 3

Gloria wants to know what Marta likes to do. Complete the conversations with the words in the chart above.

1. **GLORIA:** Do you like to listen to music?

   MARTA: Yes, I love to. I (1)_____*always*_____ listen to music.

2. **GLORIA:** Do you ever visit museums?

   MARTA: No, I (2)_____ visit museums.

3. **GLORIA:** Do you eat at restaurants?

   MARTA: I (3)_____ eat at restaurants, about three

   times a week.

4. **GLORIA:** Do you ever see plays?

   MARTA: I (4)_____ see plays. I only go to the theater

   about once or twice a year.

Practice 4

What do people in the United States do on weekends?
Write these words in order. Make sentences in your notebook.

1. *usually/like to relax/on weekends/people in the United States*

<u>   People in the United States usually like to relax on weekends.   </u>

2. *visit/friends or family/sometimes/people in the United States*

3. *children/play sports outside/usually/in hot or cold weather*

4. *with their friends/teenagers/like to go shopping/often*

5. *on the weekends/like to eat/sometimes/at restaurants/families*

Practice 5

Janet's little sister, Jessica, is like many 15-year-old girls in the United States. She does different activities during the week. Write sentences about her activities this week.

Monday	Tuesday	Wednesday	Thursday
talk on the phone		talk on the phone	read
play the piano	play the piano	play the piano	
play soccer	play soccer	play soccer	play soccer
do homework	do homework	do homework	do homework

1. (*usually*) _____ Jessica usually plays the piano. _____

2. (*always*) _____

3. (*sometimes*)_____

4. (*hardly ever*) _____

5. (*never*) _____

10   **Unit 2**

Practice 6

How do you relax? Use *always, usually, often, sometimes, hardly ever,* or *never.* Write sentences like "I always play soccer on the weekend."

1. *(play sports)* _____

2. *(go to restaurants)* _____

3. *(watch TV)* _____

4. *(play music)* _____

5. *(talk on the phone)* _____

Read, Think, and Write

Read the conversation carefully.

Visiting Friends—It's Not the Same Everywhere

JANET: Do you like to visit friends?

MARTA: Sure. But you know, it's different in the United States.
In Guadalajara, I always visit my friends. I visit them in the
morning, afternoon, or evening. Sometimes I call them first.
But often I visit without calling. Sometimes we go downtown to the clubs. But we don't need to do anything special
to have fun. We enjoy just being together and talking.

JANET: It's different in the United States.

MARTA: Yes, it is. In the United States, I always call my friends first.
Then we make plans. Sometimes there is a party. Often I
bring drinks or food with me to the party. I never do that
in Guadalajara!

JANET: You're right. People here always have plans. They are
very busy.

Practice 7

In your notebook answer these questions.

How is visiting friends in Guadalajara, Mexico, different from visiting friends in the United States?

Which is more like the way it's done in your native country—visiting friends in Guadalajara or visiting friends in the United States?

Practice 8

Think about these questions. Make notes about your thoughts.

In your native country, what do you and your friends do when you visit? Do you call first?

In the United States, what do you and your friends do when you visit? Do you call first?

Practice 9

In your notebook, write two sentences about visiting friends in your country. Then write two sentences about visiting friends in the United States. Write about which way you like better. Tell why.

CHECK YOUR LEARNING

What did you like best about this workbook unit? Why?

_____

_____

What did you learn in this workbook unit to help you at work or in your personal life?

_____

_____

PROBLEM SOLVING IN THE NEIGHBORHOOD

Spotlight on *There Is, There Are, There Was, There Were*

Present Singular	**Past Singular**
There is a kitten on the roof.	**There was** a kitten on the roof (an hour ago).
Is there a kitten on the roof?	**Was there** a kitten on the roof?
Present Plural	**Past Plural**
There are many students in the class.	**There were** many students in the class.
Are there many students in the class.	**Were there** many students in the class?

Practice I

Read the neighborhood bus schedule. Complete the passenger's questions and the driver's answers. Use *is, are, was,* or *were*. Use contractions if you can.

LOCATION	MON.–SAT.	SUNDAY
Main and Broadway	2:30 P.M.	No Bus Service
Main and Franklin	2:35 P.M.	
State and Broadway	2:50 P.M.	
Main and Broadway	2:55 P.M.	

1. **PASSENGER:** _____ there a bus at 3:30 at Main and Broadway?

   DRIVER: No, there _____ a bus at 3:30.

2. **PASSENGER:** _____ there a bus at 2:35 at Main and Franklin?

   DRIVER: Let's see. It's 2:40 now. Yes, there _____ a bus at 2:35.

3. **PASSENGER:** _____ there buses on Sundays?

   DRIVER: No, there _____ any buses on Sundays.

Practice 2

Answer the following questions in your notebook.

Are there buses in your neighborhood? Where is the nearest bus stop to your home? Which buses stop there?

Practice 3

Complete these conversations about the neighborhood map.
Use the words below.

library   bus station   bank   department store   movie theater

1. **STUDENT:**   Is there a _____ in
                         the neighborhood?

   BUS DRIVER: Yes, there is. It's on Washington Street.

2. **CUSTOMER:**   Is there a _____ in
                         the neighborhood?

   CLERK: Yes, there is. It's between Broadway Street and
                         Franklin Street.

3. **MAN:**   Is there a _____ on
                         Broadway Street?

   WAITRESS: No, there isn't. There's a bus stop.

Spotlight on Simple Past of Regular and Irregular Verbs

Use the simple past to talk about an activity completed in the past. Many simple past verbs end in -ed, but many others have an irregular past form. Here are some examples:

Regular		Irregular	
Simple Form	**Simple Past**	**Simple Form**	**Simple Past**
ask	asked	buy	bought
call	called	find	found
cook	cooked	get	got
finish	finished	go	went
play	played	say	said
stay	stayed	take	took
talk	talked	write	wrote

Practice 4

Complete these sentences about life in the neighborhood with simple past verb forms.

1. Cha-Soon (take)_____ her son to the bus stop at 7:35 A.M.

2. Last night, Margarita (write)_____ a letter to her mom.

3. Kathy (find)_____ news about her country on television.

4. At the party, Young (say)_____ hello to a new friend.

5. Margarita (get)_____ a new house.

6. She (pay)_____ $20,000 as a down payment.

7. Kathy (find)_____ a light out in her apartment.

8. Cass (write)_____ a security report every day last week.

9. Maria (get)_____ a job as a museum security guard.

10. Ray (get)_____ a job as a taxi driver in the neighborhood.

Spotlight on Prepositions of Location

The words *inside, outside, beside, between,* and *behind* tell where something or somebody is.

outside

inside

beside

between

behind

Practice 5

Complete the sentences with these prepositions of location. Look at the map on page 14.

beside   between   behind   on the corner of   next to

1. The Mekong Restaurant is _____ the Central Bank.

2. The park is _____ the Central Bank.

3. Davison's Department Store is _____ Franklin Street and Broadway Street.

4. The movie theater is _____ of Broadway Street and State Street.

Practice 6

Think about your neighborhood. Write four sentences about it in your notebook. Use the place names and the prepositions below. For example, write, "In my neighborhood there is a pay phone on the corner of 46th and University."

Place Names	Prepositions
bus stop, movie theater, supermarket, park, pay phone, currency exchange, restaurant	inside, outside, beside, in, on, between, behind, next to, across the street from

Read, Think, and Write

Read the story carefully.

Nice Neighborhood, Bad Neighbors

Manijeh, her husband, Hamid, and their three sons live in Long Beach, California. They came to the United States from Iran 15 years ago. They saved money for a long time. They both worked ten hours a day, five or six days a week. Now they live in a big four-bedroom house in a nice neighborhood. There are trees beside big houses, and there are street lights. There is also a small park. Inside the park is a swimming pool behind a tall fence.

Manijeh says she doesn't know her neighbors. They aren't friends. Sometimes she says hello to the people across the street. That's all. She doesn't like the people in the house next door. She says they are very noisy. They watch loud television shows, listen to loud music, and talk loudly outside until midnight. But she doesn't ask them to be quiet. She doesn't want to have a problem with the noisy neighbors. Is she doing the right thing? What do you think?

Practice 7

Read the story again. Complete the T-chart in your notebook.
Write about the nice neighborhood. Write about the noisy neighbors.

Nice Neighborhood	Bad Neighbors
Manijeh and her family live in a *four-bedroom house*	Next door, *there are noisy people.*

Practice 8

Think about these questions. Write your ideas in your notebook.

Do you know your neighbors? Do you talk to them about problems in your neighborhood? What things do you like about your neighborhood? What things don't you like about your neighborhood?

Practice 9

In your notebook write about your neighborhood. Write about what you like. Then write about what you don't like.

CHECK YOUR LEARNING

What did you like best about this workbook unit? Why? _____

_____

What did you learn in this workbook unit to help you at work or in your personal life?

_____

_____

Spotlight on Simple Past in Affirmative Statements

> I/You/He/She/We/They **worked** in Mexico.
>
> I/You/He/She/We/They **moved** to the United States in 1995.
>
> Regular simple past verbs end in *-ed*. Use simple past to talk about completed in the past.

Practice I

Complete the story using the simple past. Check your spelling.

Oprah Winfrey's Story

When Oprah was a young girl, she (1) *live* _____lived_____ on her

grandmother's farm. She (2) *play* _____ and

(3) *work* _____ on the farm. She didn't have many friends,

so she (4) *talk* _____ to the animals! She

(5) *like* _____ to talk. At an early age she

(6) *want* _____ to speak in front of people. When she was

only three years old, she (7) *practice* _____ speaking at

her church. People were surprised that Oprah was so good!

At first, Oprah (8) *like* _____ school, but when she

(9) *move* _____ from the farm to a big city, she

(10) *change* _____. She didn't like to study.

Oprah's father (11) *help* _____ her. Her father

(12) *watch* _____ her do her homework. He

(13) *talk* _____ to her about reading more. She did.

Oprah (14) *try* _____ to please her father. She

(15) *study* _____ and (16) *sudy* _____.

Read about Oprah Winfrey's job experience.

WORK HISTORY

Dates	Job Experience
1988 to Present	Producer and owner of Harpo Production Studio
1985 to Present	National talk-show host for *The Oprah Winfrey Show*
1985 to Present	Actress—movies and TV
1984 to 1985	Talk-show host for *A.M. Chicago* in Chicago, Illinois
1977 to 1983	Talk-show co-host in Baltimore, Maryland
1976 to 1977	TV news anchorperson and reporter in Baltimore, Maryland
1973 to 1976	TV news co-anchor in Nashville, Tennessee
1970 to 1973	Radio newscaster (part-time position) in Nashville, Tennessee

---

Practice 2

Complete the sentences about Oprah Winfrey's job experience.
Use the simple past form of the verbs below.

change   live   start   work   report   move   finish

1. Oprah _____*started*_____ her first job in 1970.

2. In 1970 she _____ in Nashville, Tennessee.

3. Oprah _____ part-time for three years.

4. She _____ in Nashville, Tennessee, from 1970 to 1976.

5. From 1976 to 1983, Oprah _____ in Baltimore, Maryland.

6. Her job _____ from reporter to talk-show host in Baltimore.

7. The name of the talk show in Chicago _____ from *A.M. Chicago* to *The Oprah Winfrey Show* in 1985.

Spotlight on Simple Past in Yes/No Questions and Negative Statements

Did Bill Gates   **live** in Ohio?   No, he **didn't**.
Did he   **work** for IBM?

Practice 3

William asked Lisa questions about different successful Americans. Write the questions and the negative answers.

WILLIAM: (1) *Roberto Clemente/play/tennis*

         _____ Did Roberto Clemente play tennis? _____

LISA: No, (2)_____ he didn't play tennis _____ He played

baseball.

WILLIAM: (3) *An Wang/start* _____

Microsoft?

LISA: No, (4)_____. Bill Gates

started it.

WILLIAM: (5) *Sandra Cisneros/have* _____

_____ her own TV show?

LISA: No, (6)_____. She writes

books.

Practice 4

Now write another question and answer about a successful American. Ask the class your question.

_____

_____

Spotlight on Past Time Expressions

Cisneros had an idea **three years ago**.
She wrote a book **last year**.

When did you **last** buy a book?
I bought one **yesterday**.

More Time Expressions:

the day before yesterday
yesterday morning/afternoon/evening
an hour/a week/a month/ago

the night before last last night/week/month
a minute/an hour/a week/a month/ago

Practice 5

Answer these questions about yourself. Use past time expressions.

1. When did you start elementary school?

    I started elementary school 18 years ago.

2. When did you move to the United States?

    _____

3. When did you get your first job?

    _____

4. When did you start to study English?

    _____

5. When did you last watch a good program on TV? What was the show?

    _____

Read, Think, and Write

Read the story carefully.

Sandra Cisneros

Sandra Cisneros is a well-known author. Her mother is Mexican American and her father was born in Mexico. Sandra was born in the United States. She writes about the people from her world. She tells the stories of poor people, especially children and women.

Cisneros came from a poor family. She was born in Chicago in 1954. There were seven children in the different apartments in Chicago. Sometimes they moved to Mexico. But they always returned to Chicago. At last they moved into a house. Cisneros wrote her first book about this house and neighborhood. The book is called *The House on Mango Street*. It was published in 1983.

The author's mother helped her to become a writer. She let Sandra read and study. Sandra loved to read. She made up stories. Even when she was a little girl, she wanted to go to college.

Cisneros went to college. Later she wrote her first book. She received prizes and honors for her work. She writes fiction, nonfiction, and poetry. Her second book, *Woman Hollering Creek*, was published in 1991. This book won the PEN Center West Award for best fiction in 1992.

Practice 6

Complete a timeline on Sandra Cisneros. Use the information from the article.

Born in Chicago

| 1954 | 1983 | 1991 | 1992 |

Practice 7

Write sentences about achievements and important events in your life.

When did you start school? _____

When did you come to the United States? _____

When did you get your first job? _____

Practice 8

Write five other events or achievements in your life. What about marriage? Children? Good friends? Success in school? Success in a job? When did the events happen? Write the years.

	Events	**When?**
1.	_____	_____
2.	_____	_____
3.	_____	_____
4.	_____	_____
5.	_____	_____

Practice 9

Now make a timeline of your life in your notebook. Use the timeline on page 23 as an example.

CHECK YOUR LEARNING

What did you like best about this workbook unit? Why? _____

_____

What did you learn in this workbook unit to help you at work or in your personal life?

_____

Spotlight on Direct Object Pronouns

Tina does aerobics. She does **them** every day.
Mark takes karate class. He takes **it** once a week.
Victor likes Marisa. He likes **her** very much.
Vera goes skating with Angelo. She goes with **him** to the park.
Our karate teacher helps **us**. She helps **you** with kicks,
and she helps **me** with form.

In the sentences above, the direct object answers
the questions *who* or *what*.

Practice 1

Complete the conversations. Use direct object pronouns.

1. **HENRI:** Are you going to go jogging today?

   MARK: Yes, I'm going to do (1)____it____ after work today.

   HENRI: Is Vera going with you?

   MARK: Uh-huh. I'm going to meet (2)_____ at her house.

   HENRI: Can I join (3)_____?

   MARK: Sure. Meet (4)_____ at Vera's house at 2:00.

2. **VICTOR:** I went to the doctor for my back. I hurt (5)_____ in

   karate class.

   ROSA: What did the doctor do?

   VICTOR: She gave me some pills. I take (6)_____ with meals. I

   like my doctor a lot. She really helps (7)_____.

Spotlight on Future with *Going To*

I **am (I'm) going to take** karate.   I **am (I'm not) going to take** aerobics.

Vera **is (Vera's) going to exercise** tomorrow.   She **is (she's) not going to exercise** today.

You **are (You're) going to jog** every day.   You **are (You're) not going to jog** at night.

We **are (We're) going to lose** weight.   We **are (We're) not going to eat** too much.

Laura and Angelo **are going to eat** well.   They **are (They're) not going to eat** junk food.

Use *going to* + verb to talk about things in the near future.

Practice 2

Laura and Angelo work for the water department. They get ten days off
with pay a year—eight sick days for illness or injury and two personal days.
The personal days are for doctors' appointments, business appointments,
or personal reasons. Read the information. Then complete the sentences.
Tell if Laura and Angelo are going to use *a sick day* or *a personal day*.

1. Angelo hurt his leg.

   _____ He is going to use a sick day. _____

2. Laura has a doctor's appointment.

   _____

3. They have the flu.

   _____

4. Laura has a long appointment at the bank.

   _____

5. Laura has to stay home with her sick baby.

   _____

6. Angelo and Laura want to go to a big baseball game.

   _____

Practice 3

Complete the conversation. Use *going to* and a contraction of *be*.

ANGEL: Guess what, Tina? (1) I ____I'm going to____ start a diet.

TINA: So, when are you going to start?

ANGEL: (2) I _____ start Monday. (3) I _____

eat less meat and more vegetables. (4) My wife

_____ help me. (5) *She* _____ cook

less fried food. 6) *We/not* _____ buy candy and

ice cream either.

Practice 4

Complete the story. Use *going to* and the verbs below.

Next week I (1) *visit* ____am going to visit____ Los Angeles. My

sister lives there. She (2) *take* _____ me to the

beach and to Hollywood. We (3) *have* _____ a

wonderful time.

Then, next fall my sister (4) *visit* _____ me in

New York. I (5) *cook* _____ her favorite foods.

My brothers (6) *come* _____ to my house, and

we (7) *eat* _____ together.

Spotlight on Count and Noncount Nouns

Count Noun	Noncount Nouns
How **many hours** of sleep do you get?	How **much exercise** does Vera get?
I sleep **a few hours** every night.	She gets **a little** exercise.
I sleep **many** hours every night.	She gets **a lot of** exercise.

Practice 5

Complete the sentences. Use *many, much, a lot of, a few,* or *a little.*

MARK: What's wrong? You look sick.

VICTOR: I'm just tired.

MARK: How (1)_____many_____ hours of sleep do you

usually get?

VICTOR: Only (2)_____. I can't sleep well.

MARK: How (3)_____ exercise do you get?

VICTOR: Not much. But I do get (4)_____ exercise now

and then.

MARK: Do you take time to relax during the week?

VICTOR: No. But I always take (5)_____ time to relax on

the weekend.

MARK: You can call in sick to work. How (6)_____

sick days do you have?

VICTOR: I haven't used any, so I have (7)_____ sick

days left.

Read, Think, and Write

Read the story carefully.

Henri's Decision

Henri went to the doctor. He was having pains in his chest. The doctor checked his heart. He also checked his cholesterol level. He asked him some questions. The doctor said, "Henri, you need to watch your health. You have risk factors for heart disease. I'm going to give you a plan for better health. It's important to follow the plan."

Henri is worried about heart disease. He is going to follow the doctor's advice. Each week he is going to add one more healthy habit. Here is Henri's plan.

Week 1: Sleep 7 1/2 hours a night. Go to bed at the same time every night.

Week 2: Don't eat salty foods. Don't add salt to food.

Week 3: Exercise regularly. Walk for 15 minutes two times a week.

Week 4: Don't eat fried foods. Eat red meat only twice a week.

Practice 6

Write four sentences about Henri's plans for the four weeks. Use *going to*.

1. In week 1,_____ Henri is going to sleep 7 1/2 hours every night._____

2. In week 2,_____

3. _____

4. _____

Practice 7

What healthy habits can you start? Think about diet, exercise, and sleep. List three habits you want to start.

1. _____

2. _____

3. _____

Practice 8

Now make your own health time line for four weeks. Add one healthy habit each week.

Week 1   Week 2   Week 3   Week 4

CHECK YOUR LEARNING

What did you like best about this workbook unit? Why?

_____

_____

What did you learn in this workbook unit to help you at work or in your personal life?

_____

_____

Spotlight on *How Much* and *How Many*

How many	children do you have?	**How much**	money does he owe?
	pets does Alex have?		rent do you pay?
	bedrooms are there?		is the deposit?

Use *how many* before count nouns in questions.
Use *how much* before noncount nouns in questions.

Practice 1

Complete the conversations. Use *how much* or *how many*.

ALEX: I want to rent an apartment. (1)_____

money does a large one-bedroom cost?

MANAGER: About $575 a month. How long will you want

the apartment?

ALEX: I'd like the apartment for a year. (2)_____ is

the security deposit? And can I have pets?

MANAGER: The security deposit is $350. (3)_____ pets

do you have?

ALEX: Well, uh, a few pets.

LINDA: I'd like to look for a house in Corona.

AGENT: (4)_____ bedrooms do you want?

LINDA: Three. And we need two bathrooms.

AGENT: (5)_____ money can you pay for the house?

LINDA: I'm not sure. (6)_____ do three-bedroom

houses cost?

Spotlight on Future with *Will*

I'll = I will   *I won't = I will not*

I **will talk** to a real estate agent   I **will not** talk to an agent.
I'll talk to a real estate agent.   I **won't talk** to an agent.

I/You/He/She/We/They **will look** at townhouses.
I/You/He/She/We/They **won't look** at townhouses.

Use *will* + verb to talk about the future.

Practice 2

How will people live in the year 2050? Read the ideas. Circle Agree or Disagree. If you disagree, cross out the sentence. Write the correct sentence in your notebook.

People will drive cars.

1. ~~People won't drive cars.~~	Agree	(Disagree)
2. Young people will use computers and go to school at home.	Agree	Disagree
3. Everyone will live in apartments.	Agree	Disagree
4. Some people will live to be 130.	Agree	Disagree
5. Families will be smaller.	Agree	Disagree
6. The weather will never change.	Agree	Disagree
7. There won't be wars.	Agree	Disagree
8. There will be a woman president.	Agree	Disagree
9. The police won't use guns.	Agree	Disagree
10. Every home will have a garden.	Agree	Disagree

Spotlight on Wh-Question Words

Use question words to find out information.

who = people   **when** = times   **where** = places

what = things   **why** = reasons   **how** = ways

When you speak, you can use the contractions *who's (who is)* and *when's (when is)*.

Practice 3

Read the story on the organization Habitat for Humanity. Then find answers to the questions. Write the answers in your notebook.

The 12 members of the Martinez family are happy. Before, they lived in a small apartment with two bedrooms and one bathroom. Now they have a house in Orange County, California, with five bedrooms, two bathrooms, and a front yard.

The organization Habitat for Humanity helps families with little money. Habitat for Humanity builds homes for people in many parts of the United States. Habitat for Humanity's *volunteers* are people who work without pay to help other people. They built a dream home for the Martinez family, and the Martinez family helped them build it.

1. What organization helped the Martinez family?

2. Where is the Martinez family's new house?

3. Why did the Martinez family need a new house?

4. Who built the home?

5. What are volunteers?

Practice 4

Now, in your notebook, write the story again using the contractions *who's, when's, where's,* and *what's.*

Practice 5

Read the ad. Then answer the questions about it.

> **Townhouse for Sale** 4 bedrooms, 2 baths, modern kitchen with large family room. Near downtown. Only $185,000. Open House 12:00–4:00 Sunday. Call Ofelia Gomez (512) 585-1737. Newton Realty

1. Where's the townhouse? _____

2. When's the open house?_____

3. Who's the person to call about the townhouse? _____

4. What's the price of the townhouse? _____

Read, Think, and Write

Read the story carefully.

For a long time, Linda and her husband Paul wanted a new home very much. They went to a real estate agent for help. They looked for a year to find a home. They never found a place they liked. The best houses were too expensive. The other houses had problems. Some houses were too small. Others were far from schools.

Finally, Linda had an idea. She talked to her husband. They made a plan. They won't buy a new place. They will improve their apartment. They will paint their bedroom. And they will put flower pots outside their door. Linda plans to buy a new couch and a lamp for their living room. Paul will make a new table for the kitchen, and Linda will paint it blue. They will buy bright pictures for one of the kitchen walls. Now they are excited about their little dream home.

Practice 6

Make an idea map of Linda and Paul's ideas for improving their apartment. Write notes in the circles. Look at the story again for help.

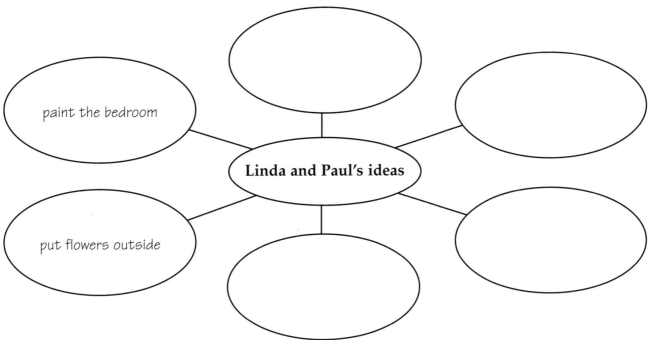

paint the bedroom

Linda and Paul's ideas

put flowers outside

Practice 7

In your notebook, write seven sentences about Linda and Paul's ideas. Use *will*, *'ll*, and *won't* in all your sentences. For example, write, "Linda and Paul will paint their bedroom."

Practice 8

Do you want to improve your home or apartment? Think about these questions.

Why do you want to improve something in your home?

What new things can you buy for your home?   OR

What can you make for your home?

Where can you put plants or flowers?   OR

Where can you put new furniture?

Where can you buy new things?   OR

Who can help you improve your home or apartment?

When can you improve your home or apartment?

Practice 9

Write answers in the idea map.

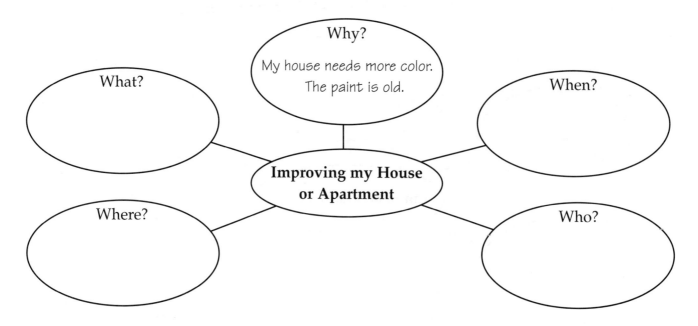

Practice 10

In your notebook, write five sentences about your plans. Your idea map will help you organize your sentences.

CHECK YOUR LEARNING

What did you like best about this workbook unit? Why?

_____

_____

What did you learn in this workbook unit to help you at work or in your personal life?

_____

_____

GETTING AROUND: PUBLIC AND PRIVATE TRANSPORTATION

Spotlight on *Need to* and *Have to*

Need to + verb

I/ You/ We/They	**need to wait for**	the bus.
I/ You/ We/They	**do not need to take**	the bus.
He/She	**needs to call**	transit information.
He/She	**doesn't need to get**	change.

Have to + verb

I/ You/ We/ They	**have to walk**	home.
I/You/ We/ They	**don't have to go**	now.
He/ She	**has to call**	a taxi.
He/ She	**doesn't have to ride**	a bicycle.

Practice 1

Complete the paragraph. Use the words below and *need to* and *have to*.

bus stop   transfer   wait   buses   change   cross street

If you call transit information, you (1)_____ know the

(2)_____. Then you (3)_____ have exact

(4)_____ to pay the fare. You (5)_____ stand

at the (6)_____ and sometimes you have to

(7)_____ forever! On the bus, you (8)_____

ask the driver for a (9)_____ if you are going to change

to another bus. In some cities you don't (10)_____ pay

for a transfer, but in other cities you do. (11)_____ are

cheap. Many people (12)_____ take them to work and to

school. Try it. You'll like it!

Practice 2

What do you have to do tomorrow? Check the list.

✓	get dressed		do the dishes
	walk to school		do the laundry
	go to work		cook dinner
	get up early		go to the bank
	drive a car		ride a bus
	ride a train		ask for a transfer
	ride a bicycle		walk home

Practice 3

When do you have to do the things you checked—in the morning, afternoon, or evening? In your notebook write complete sentences. For example, write, "I have to get dressed tomorrow morning."

Practice 4

Look again at your list in Practice 2. What things don't you have to do tomorrow? Write four more complete sentences in your notebook. For example, write, "I don't have to go to the bank tomorrow morning."

Practice 5

Now write two questions to a friend about daily activities. For example, write, "When do you have to do your laundry?"

_____

_____

Spotlight on Present Continuous

Am/*is*/*are* + a verb ending in *-ing* show an action that is happening now.

Are you **studying** English this year?   Yes, I **am**.

Is Lilia **going** to the grocery store?   No, she**'s not**. She**'s going** to the mall.

Am/*is*/*are* + a verb ending in *-ing* can also tell about an action that will happen soon.

Are you **coming** to the dance tomorrow?   Yes, I **am**.

Is Pablo **walking** to work today?   No, he **isn't**. He**'s taking** the bus.

Practice 6

Rosie works as a babysitter for the Johnson family. Mrs. Johnson calls to see how the family is doing. Complete the conversation. Change the verbs to present continuous. Remember to put forms of *be* first in a question. For example, write, "Are you buying a car?"

MRS. JOHNSON: Hi, Rosie. How (1) *you/do* _____*are you doing?*_____

ROSIE: Hello, Mrs. Johnson. (2) *we/do* _____

fine. The kids are busy.

MRS. JOHNSON: (3) *Ashley/do* _____ her homework?

ROSIE: Yes, (4) *she/read* _____ her English book.

MRS. JOHNSON: What (5) *others/do* _____?

(6) *they/watch* _____ TV?

ROSIE: Yes. Did you find a new car yet?

MRS. JOHNSON: Not yet. But (7) *we/look* _____.

ROSIE: (8) *you/come* _____ home at 10:00?

MRS. JOHNSON: Yes, (9) *we/come* _____ home early

tonight.

Spotlight on *Could* and *Would* for Requests

Questions

Could you give me a ride?
Would you hand me that map, **please**?
Would you **please** help me?

Possible Answers

Affirmative: Of course. /Yes./Sure./No problem.
Negative: No, I can't./Sorry, I can't.

You can use *could* and *would* to form polite requests. You can add *please* to make a request even more polite.

Practice 7

Bassam is trying to get to work as quickly as possible. Complete the dialogue. Use *could* and *would*.

BASSAM: Excuse me. (1)_____ you tell me where the

train station is?

NEIGHBOR: Yes, but the trains aren't running today. I just heard it

on the radio.

BASSAM: Well, I need to find a quick way to work.

(2)_____ you tell me where the bus

station is?

NEIGHBOR: Sure, but the buses around here are very slow.

BASSAM: I really need to hurry. (3)_____ you please

help me?

NEIGHBOR: (4)_____ you tell me where you work?

BASSAM: I work near the office building on Clark and Adams,

downtown.

NEIGHBOR: Me, too. Why don't you come with me? I have to leave right now, though. (5)_____ you be ready in five minutes?

BASSAM: Sure. Thanks a lot.

Read, Think, and Write

Read the story about Gina Gomez's plans.

Gina Gomez, age 19, lives in Los Angeles, California. She came to the United States from Mexico six months ago. She goes to English classes every day. Sometimes she gets a ride to school with her cousin, Manny. Other days, she walks or takes the bus. But Gina doesn't like to walk or wait for the bus. And she doesn't like to ask her cousin for a ride. She needs to get a driver's license and a used car to be independent. She wants to drive herself to work.

She has to study the California Driver's Manual, a book from the State Department of Motor Vehicles. The book will teach her driving rules. Then she has to pass a test and get a learner's permit. Next she needs to practice driving with her cousin on the freeway and on city streets. Finally, she has to take a driving test with an officer of the Department of Motor Vehicles. She needs to do well to get her driver's license. For now, she is saving money and studying English. She really wants to be independent!

Practice 8

To get her driver's license, Gina needs to do many things.
What are they? Complete the sentences.

a. First, _____ *she needs to learn English* _____.

b. After that, _____.

c. Then, _____.

d. Next, _____.

e. Later, _____.

f. Finally, _____.

Practice 9

Look at the T-chart below. Copy the chart in your notebook, but make it bigger. In your chart write about Gina's life. On the left side, write things she wants to do. On the right side, write things she needs to do.

Wants to	Needs to
She wants to get a driver's license.	She needs to study for the learner's permit test.

Practice 10

Now think about your life in the United States. Think about transportation, but also about school, health care, your family, a job, the place you live in, and so on. Do you want to be more independent in the future? How will your independent life be? Write ideas in the T-chart below.

My Life Now	A More Independent Life in the Future

Practice 11

Now, in your notebook write a paragraph about your plans to be independent.

CHECK YOUR LEARNING

What did you like best about this unit? Why? _____

_____

What did you learn in this unit to help you at work or in your personal life?

_____

YOUR LIBRARY AND OTHER COMMUNITY SERVICES

Spotlight on *Should* and *Shouldn't*

I/You/He/She/We/You/They **should** read more.
I/You/He/She/We/You/They **shouldn't** watch so much TV.

Practice 1

While walking to the library, Steve asked Carlos about his family. Complete the sentences with *should* or *shouldn't*.

STEVE: So how's your family today?

CARLOS: Oh, my mother is OK, but she's lonely.

STEVE: She (1)_____ call my mother.

How's your sister?

CARLOS: My sister still feels tired all the time.

STEVE: She (2)_____ take it easy.

CARLOS: I know, but she's busy with the kids.

STEVE: You're their uncle. You (3)_____

help your sister.

CARLOS: You're right. I (4)_____ help her more.

STEVE: What about your grandfather?

CARLOS: He's home. He (5)_____ watch so much TV.

STEVE: I agree. He (6)_____ get out and meet people.

Hey, we (7)_____ hurry. We need to get to the

library before it closes!

Practice 2

Complete the sentences. Use *should* or *shouldn't* and the words below.

walk in the park   play on the playground   see a doctor

get a library card   watch TV   talk to the librarian

go to school   go to the dentist   smoke

1. I need more English for my job. I _____ study at school.

2. Carlos's mother looks out the window. She _____.

3. I have a toothache. You _____.

4. Carlos's sister is pregnant. She _____.

5. You need to do your homework. You _____.

6. Carlos and Steve have questions about the library. They _____

_____.

7. Carlos's niece likes to read. She _____.

8. Carlos's nephew plays video games. He _____.

9. My friend likes cigarettes, but he is sick many times a year. He _____

_____.

Practice 3

Your friend is bored. She has nothing to do. She is homesick too.
She sits and thinks about her family in her country. She needs your
advice. What should she do? Write three sentences. Use *should* or
shouldn't. For example, write, "She should write a letter to her family."

1. _____

2. _____

3. _____

Spotlight on Demonstrative Pronouns
This, That, These, and *Those*

Singular

This is a book.

That's a book.

Plural

These are magazines.

Those are magazines.

Use *this* and *these* to talk about something near.
Use *that* and *those* to talk about something far away.

That's = That is There are no other contractions for these four words.

Practice 4

Gloria comes home from the library. On her table are the things she borrowed from the library. Complete the paragraph. Use *this, that, these,* and *those.*

(1)_____This_____ is my library card. On this side of the table are

things for me. On (2)_____ side are things for my

boyfriend, Allen. (3)_____ magazine is for me. I want to

show Allen (4)_____ car magazines because he's buying

a new car. (5)_____ history books are for me, and

(6)_____ travel books are for Allen. We can read

(7)_____ travel books together and watch

(8)_____ travel video about Brazil together.

(9)_____ two cassette tapes are for me to study English

at home. Allen's going to help me with my English too. With

(10)_____ library card, I borrowed great things! My

boyfriend should get a library card too!

Read, Think, and Write

Read the story.

At the Library: Using the Internet and More

We are students from Mr. Grant's Vocational English as a Second Language Laboratory, or VESL lab. Last month Mr. Grant asked us if we use the Internet in the library. Then he asked us if we use the library to borrow books. We didn't answer because we didn't know anything about the library.

The next week, Ms. Baker came to talk to the class about the library. She is a teacher and a librarian. All the students filled out library card applications. We all got library cards. Mr. Grant told us to go to the public library near our homes and try the Internet.

Julio and I went to the library together. We were a little nervous. We didn't understand the library computers. We didn't know how to use the Internet. We asked the librarian to help us. She showed us how to use the Internet. In the library we found a lot of books, newspapers, and magazines. We saw CDs and videos there too.

Now we go twice a week to the library. We really enjoy it. We are getting information about our countries—Costa Rica and Colombia—on the Internet. The library is a good place to spend leisure time.

> Verner Elizondo
> Julio Cesar Osorio

Practice 5

Circle the correct answer to the questions.

1. At the beginning of the story, how many students used the Internet at the library?　　　0　　2　　all

2. At the beginning, how many students borrowed books from the library?　　　0　　2　　all

3. After Ms. Baker talked to the class, how many students got library cards?　　　0　　2　　all

4. Do Verner and Julio use the Internet now?　　　yes　　no

Practice 6

Now think about things you can use at the library. Write them on the idea map below.

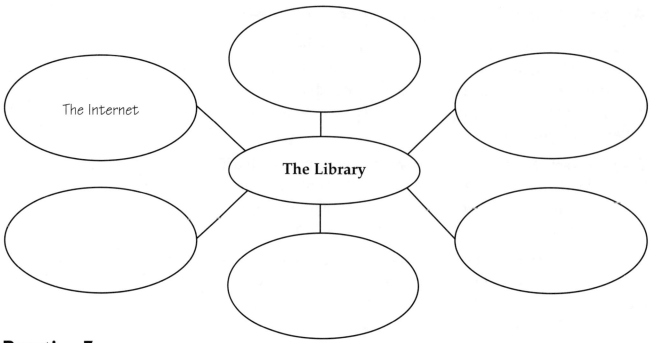

The Internet

The Library

Practice 7

Now write three sentences about the library. Use your idea map and these words to help you: *borrow, read, listen to, watch, use.* For example, write, " I can borrow books for my children."

1. _____

2. _____

3. _____

CHECK YOUR LEARNING

What did you like best about this workbook unit? Why? _____

_____

What did you learn in this workbook unit to help you at work or in your personal life?

_____

_____

Spotlight on Meanings of *Can* and *Can't*

Ability/Skills

Statements   Questions

I/You/He/She/We/They **can** type.   **Can** you type?
                              can't

Giving Permission   **Asking for Permission**

You **can** take this book.   **Can** I smoke?

Refusing Permission/Expressing Rules

You **can't** smoke here.   He **can't** leave work early.

Practice 1

Siu works at Braidwood Industries. Read the list of company rules. Tell what he *can* or *can't* do. Complete the sentences.

1. Siu _____ go to work late or leave early.

2. He _____ eat lunch between 12:00 and 1:00.

3. Siu _____ eat at his desk.

4. If Siu's family has an emergency, they _____ call him at work.

5. If overtime is approved, Siu _____ work it.

6. Siu likes cigars, but he _____ smoke inside the building.

BRAIDWOOD INDUSTRIES

- Employees work from 9:00 to 5:00.

- Employees eat lunch from 12:00 to 1:00 in the cafeteria. Please do not eat at your desk.

- Employees should not receive personal phone calls, except in emergencies.

- Employees are allowed to work overtime if it is approved the day before.

- Smoking is not allowed inside the building.

Spotlight on Compound Sentences with And ... Too and And ... Either

Affirmative Sentences

I can use a computer, **and** I can communicate well **too.**
Jose landscapes, **and** he cleans houses **too.**

Negative Sentences

I can't work evenings, **and** I can't work weekends **either.**
They can't pay a mechanic, **and** they can't repair their car **either**

Use *and too* to combine two affirmative sentences.
Use *and either* to combine two negative sentences.

Practice 2

Write sentences about these people. Use *and ... too* to combine two positive sentences. Use *and ... either* to combine two negative sentences. Look at the box above for examples.

Abilities	Siu	Tony	Alfredo	Thuy	Paul
Use a calculator	yes	no			no
Work evenings		no	yes		no
Landscape			yes	yes	
Repair computers	yes			yes	

1. Siu _____ can use a calculator and repair computers too _____.

2. Tony _____.

3. Alfredo _____.

4. Thuy _____.

5. Paul _____.

Spotlight on *Must and Must Not*

I/You/He/She/We/They   **must** provide three references.
The references   **must not** be relatives.

Must has the same form for all persons. *Must* in the affirmative means "have to."

Must not means "It is not permitted." Use *must* in formal contexts to express obligation.

Practice 3

Complete the paragraph below. Use *must* or *must not.*

When you fill out a job application, you (1)_____

write neatly. You (2)_____ answer all the questions,

but you (3)_____ lie about your experience.

You (4)_____ always be honest. If you get an interview,

you (5)_____ dress well and be on time.

You (6)_____ be late for your interview.

Practice 4

Read the information. Then complete the sentences using *must* or *must not.*

1. You _____ go to the workshop between 6:30 and 9:00.

2. You _____ get an application from your teacher.

3. You _____ return the application to your teacher.

4. Applications _____ be turned in by Friday, March 27.

5. You _____ enter the workshop without permission.

**COME TO THE
JOB SEARCH WORKSHOP!**

**Wednesday, April 1, in Room 33
from 6:30 to 9:00 P.M.**

Get an application from
your teacher.

Return it to the secretary in the
main office by Friday, March 27.

Do not enter the workshop
without permission.

See you there!

Spotlight on *Must* and *Have to*

Must and **have to**

More Formal		Less Formal
You **must** provide three references.	=	You **have to** provide three references.
Must not		
Your references **must not** be relatives.	=	It is not permitted to use relatives as references.
Don't have to		
You **don't have to** take the drug test twice.	=	You don't need to take it twice.

In the affirmative, *must* and *have to* are almost the same; *must* is more formal. The negative is very different: use *must not* to mean something is not permitted; use *don't have to* to mean something is not necessary.

Practice 5

Alfredo is new at your school. Tell him what he *must* do, what he *must not* do, and what he *doesn't have to* do.

1. Alfredo _____ wear formal clothes to class.

2. He _____ bring a radio to class.

3. He _____ forget to do his homework.

4. Alfredo _____ speak English in class.

5. He _____ memorize new words right away.
   The teacher will give him extra time.

6. Alfredo _____ copy answers during a test. The teacher
   will be angry.

7. Alfredo _____ stand up when the teacher comes in.

8. He _____ listen to the other students and the teacher.

Read, Think, and Write

Read the story carefully.

A Busy Volunteer

Hien Pham has an interesting job. Hien is a volunteer teacher. He doesn't get paid. He teaches people to speak and write in Vietnamese.

Hien has many good job skills. He can speak Vietnamese, and he can speak English too. In his job he has to communicate well in two languages. He must work well with people. In Vietnam, Hien was a business owner. He owned a T-shirt shop. He liked to help his customers choose good T-shirts.

He can do volunteer work weekday mornings and he can work Saturdays too. He can't work week nights, and he can't work Sundays either. He has to go to night class Monday through Thursday to learn more English. On Sundays he goes to church in the morning, and he has to babysit his nephew in the afternoon. He is busy, but happy.

Hien wants to be an English teacher, and he wants to study computers too. He wants a job that uses all his job skills.

Practice 6

Answer these questions about Hien Pham. Use the answers below.

Yes, he does.	Yes, he can.	Yes, he was.	Yes, he did.
No, he doesn't.	No, he can't.	No, he wasn't.	No, he didn't.

1. Does he have a job now? _____.

2. Did he work in his country? _____.

3. Was he a teacher in Vietnam? _____.

4. Was he a business owner in Vietnam _____.

5. Does he have to communicate well? _____.

6. Does he have to speak English? _____.

Practice 7

Think about these questions.

What kind of job do you want?

What job skills do you have to have to get it?

How much money do you want to be paid?

How much job experience should you have to be paid that amount?

What job skills do you want to have?

Where do you have to go to get those skills?

Practice 8

Now organize your ideas about the first question. Write them in the circles on the idea map below.

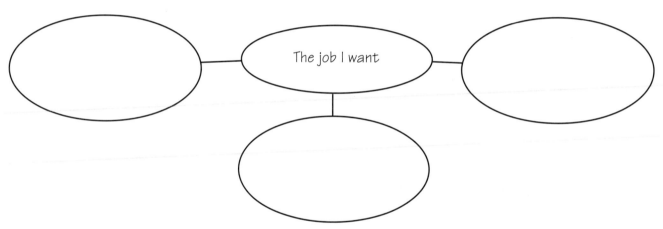

The job I want

Practice 9

In your notebook write three sentences about your job skills.

CHECK YOUR LEARNING

What did you like best about this workbook unit?_____

_____.

What did you learn in this workbook unit to help you at work or in your personal life?

_____.

_____.

Spotlight on Indirect Objects

Indirect object with for/to	OR	**Indirect object without** for/to
Mei bought a table **for Tom.**		Mei bought **Tom** a table.
Mei bought a table **for him**.		Mei bought **him** a table.
They mailed the receipt **to Mei**.		They mailed **Mei** the receipt.
They mailed the receipt **to her**.		They mailed **her** the receipt.
Gary gave the book to **me/you**		Gary gave **me/you/him/her**
/him/her/us/them.		**us/them** the book.

Practice 1

Complete these sentences with *to* or *for*.

Mei helped Tom with his new shop. She bought a table
and lamp (1)_____ him. She also ordered a couch
(2)_____ him. The store sent the couch (3)_____
them right away.

Tom was really pleased. He cooked a delicious dinner
(4)_____ Mei. He also gave flowers (5)_____ her
when she sat down to eat.

Practice 2

Look at the short form of indirect objects which do not use *for* or *to*
in the chart. In your notebook, copy the story using this form.
For example, write, "She bought him a table and lamp."

Spotlight on Comparative Adjectives

Her lamp is small. My lamp is **smaller**.
The brown desk is big. The black desk is **bigger**.
This chair is **better than** the other chair.
Ken's garage is **dirtier than** our garage.
Their couch is **more expensive**.
Our computer is **less powerful** than Jack's.

big–bigger good–better dirty–dirtier expensive–more expensive

To compare things or people, add *-er* to most adjectives with one syllable. For most adjectives with two or more syllables, use *more* or *less*.

Practice 3

Complete the sentences with comparative adjectives.

NICOLE: Let's go to the second-hand store on Broadway today.

JUDY: Why not the discount store? The discount store is

          (1) *big* _____bigger_____ than the second-hand store.

NICOLE: But things are (2) *expensive* _____ at the

          discount store.

JUDY: True. The second-hand store is less expensive. But the

          discount store has a (3) *good* _____ selection.

NICOLE: The second-hand store is (4) *close* _____.

          It's a (5) *long* _____ drive to the discount store.

JUDY: But it takes a long time to find things at the second-hand

          store. It's (6) *fast* _____ to find things in the

          discount store.

NICOLE: Here's an idea. We could go to both stores for a while.

Practice 4

Mei and Tom are comparing two places for Tom's new shop.
Complete the story with comparative adjectives.

Shop on Third Avenue	Shop on Orange Street
800 square feet	650 square feet
30 years old	modern
free parking available	no free parking available
20 miles from home	close to home
not many people	crowded area
$1000 per month rent	$875 per month rent

Tom: I like the shop on Orange Street. It's (1) *modern*

_____more modern_____ than the one on Third Avenue.

Mei: I know the Third Avenue shop is (2) *old* _____.

But Third Avenue is a (3) *busy* _____ area.

You could get more customers.

Tom: But what about the rent? The shop on Orange is

(4) *cheap* _____.

Mei: You're right, Third Avenue is (5) *expensive* _____.

But you could really use the extra space.

Tom: Don't forget. Orange is (6) *close* _____ to home.

Mei: What about the parking? Parking is free at Third Avenue.

Tom: Do you really think Third Avenue is a (7) *good*

_____ place?

Mei: I do. Couldn't we talk with the building manager?

Spotlight on *Could*

> *Could* has three different meanings.
>
> 1. They **could** buy a new table next week, or they **could** buy a desk.
>
> Use *could* to talk about future possibility.
>
> 2. Mei **couldn't** move the big couch yesterday, but Matt **could** move it.
>
> Use *could* to show ability in the past.
>
> 3. **Could** you help us? **Could** I see the manager?
>
> Use *could* for requests.

Practice 5

Think of two answers to each question. Use *could* in your answers.

1. I want to visit my brother in New York, but my car isn't working.

   What should I do?

   a. _____ You could take _____   *or*   b. _____ You could take _____

   _____ the bus. _____   _____ the train _____

2. My wife and I want to buy a car, but we don't have enough money. What should we do?

   a. _____   *or*   b. _____

   _____   _____

3. My friend gave me her old car. She didn't want any money for the gift. How can I thank her?

   a. _____   *or*   b. _____

   _____   _____

4. My brother wants to come to the United States with his family.
He needs a place to live. My apartment is very small. What can I do?

a. _____   or   b. _____

_____   _____

5. I need a desk for my computer. I only have $60. What should I do?

a. _____   or   b. _____

_____   _____

Read, Think, and Write

Read the story carefully.

Nicole's Plan

Nicole had a big problem. Two years ago she got a credit card with 18 percent interest per year. Soon she owed $2000 on the card. It took a long time to pay the bill. She paid $500 extra in interest, and she paid a $40 fee to have the credit card for a year.

Nicole decided to plan how to spend her money. She made a budget. She didn't want any more money problems. Nicole also didn't want to buy things on credit again. Now she spends $900 a month on rent, transportation, medicine, and food. After that, she spends money on extras like clothes, a vacation, presents, and fun things. She has an average of $150 a month to spend on extras. Each month, she can buy something different. She knows she doesn't need everything at one time.

Here is her budget for her extras:

August	go on a trip: $100
September	buy new fall clothes: $150
October	buy a new TV: $200
November	buy Christmas presents: $150

Practice 6

Complete Nicole's extras budget time line.

$100 for a trip

August   September   October   November

Practice 7

How much do you spend each month on housing, transportation,

medicine, and food? _____

Practice 8

Now think about the extra things you could buy in the next five
months, like clothes, a vacation, presents, and fun things. Write the
extras and the cost for each in your notebook.

Practice 9

How much do you spend on extras a month? _____

In your notebook make your own budget. See Nicole's plan
for some ideas.

CHECK YOUR LEARNING

What did you like best about this workbook unit? Why?

_____

_____

What did you learn in this workbook unit to help you at work or in
your personal life?

_____

_____